For free work sheets for this book, please email us at

<u>sisters@holyassumptionmonastery.com</u>

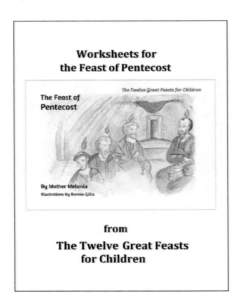

Or go to
<u>bookconnect.review/dp/pentecostworksheets</u>

Looking for Pascha (Easter) books?

Pascha at the Duck Pond -

A whimsical look at how to prepare and how NOT to prepare for Pascha.

go to bit.ly/Pascha-Duck-Pond

Pascha, the Feast of Feasts

from *The Three-Day Pascha series*

Be glad today! Be glad! Rejoice!
With all creation, lift your voice,
For Christ has died, but lives again –
Restoring life to fallen men.

go to bit.ly/Pascha-Feast

The Feast of Pentecost

from *The Twelve Great Feasts for Children*

Published by Holy Assumption Monastery
1519 Washington St.
Calistoga, CA 94515

Phone: (707) 942-6244
Website: https://holyassumptionmonastery.com
Email: sisters@holyassumptionmonastery.com

The Feast of Pentecost
from *The Twelve Great Feasts for Children*

by Mother Melania
(first published under her former name – Sister Elayne)

HOLY ASSUMPTION MONASTERY
Calistoga, California

THE TWELVE GREAT FEASTS FOR CHILDREN series:

In the Orthodox Church Year, the Feast of Feasts, in a class by itself, is the Resurrection. After the Resurrection in importance come the twelve Great Feasts. These feasts are the Church's celebration of, and participation in, key events leading to our salvation. The Great Feasts are often separated into Feasts of the Lord and Feasts of the Theotokos.

Feasts of the Lord

Exaltation of the Cross
Nativity of Our Lord (Christmas)
Theophany of Our Lord (Epiphany)
Entry of Our Lord into Jerusalem (Palm Sunday)
Ascension of Our Lord
Pentecost
Transfiguration of Our Lord

Feasts of the Theotokos

Nativity of the Theotokos
Entry of the Theotokos into the Temple
Meeting of Our Lord*
    (Presentation of Christ in the Temple)
Annunciation
Dormition of the Theotokos

* The Meeting of Our Lord is also considered a Feast of the Lord

A final note - Theotokos, an ancient title for the Virgin Mary, means "birthgiver of God." Used since at least the third century, this title guards the truth that Mary's Son is not only fully human, but fully God.

The Feast of Pentecost is celebrated 50 days after Pascha (Easter)

Blessed art Thou,
  O Christ Our God
Thou hast revealed the
  fishermen as most wise
By sending down upon them
  the Holy Spirit
Through them Thou didst draw
  the world into Thy net
O Lover of Man,
  Glory to Thee!

-Troparion of the Feast of Pentecost

Be glad! Be glad! For on this day
God's Spirit comes to light our way,
To guide us in through Christ the Door,
To dwell in us forevermore.

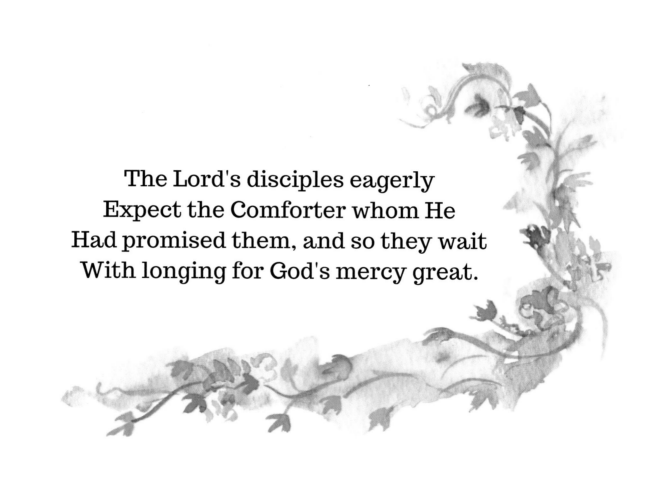

The Lord's disciples eagerly
Expect the Comforter whom He
Had promised them, and so they wait
With longing for God's mercy great.

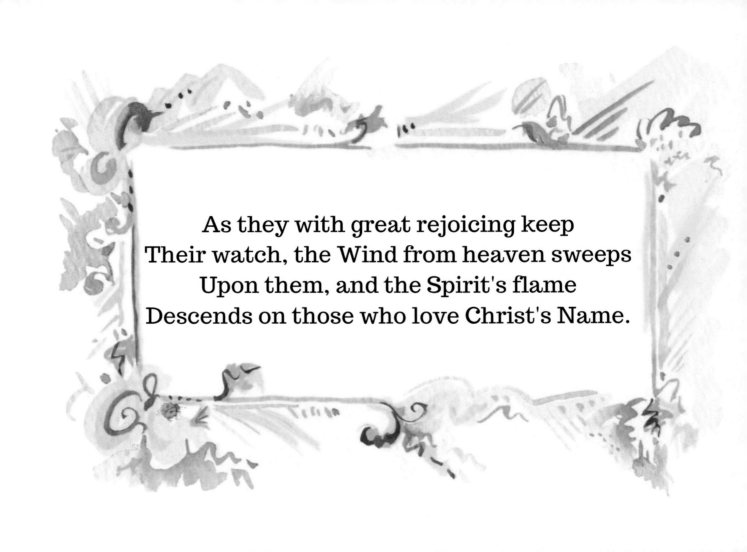

As they with great rejoicing keep
Their watch, the Wind from heaven sweeps
Upon them, and the Spirit's flame
Descends on those who love Christ's Name.

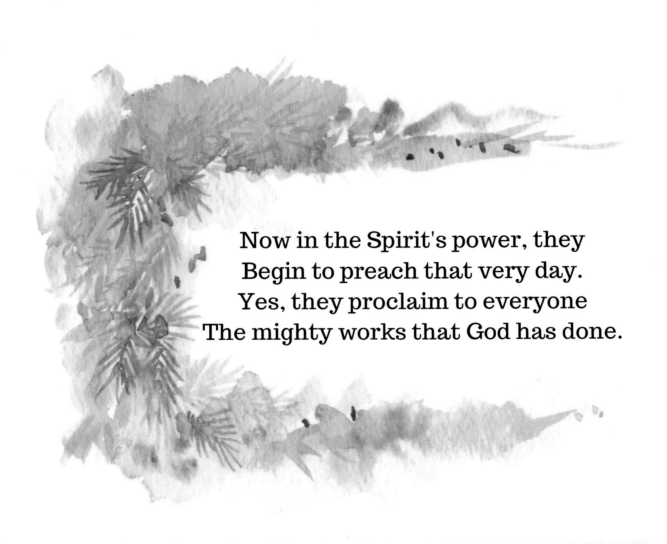

Now in the Spirit's power, they
Begin to preach that very day.
Yes, they proclaim to everyone
The mighty works that God has done.

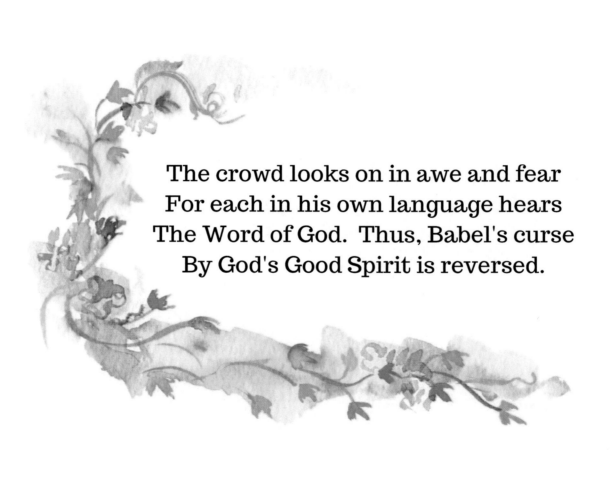

The crowd looks on in awe and fear
For each in his own language hears
The Word of God. Thus, Babel's curse
By God's Good Spirit is reversed.

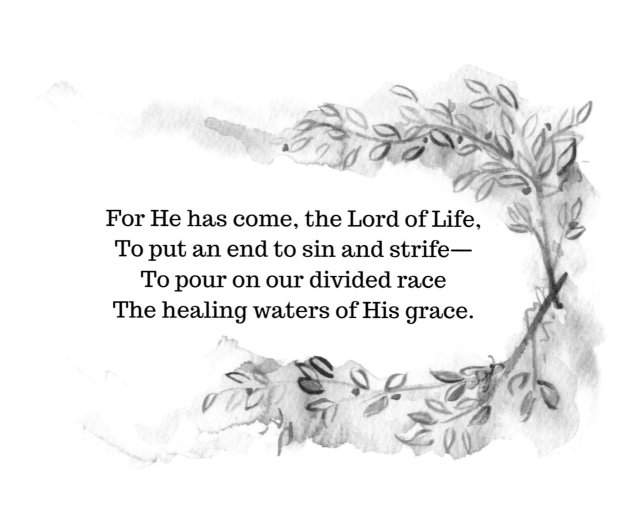

For He has come, the Lord of Life,
To put an end to sin and strife—
To pour on our divided race
The healing waters of His grace.

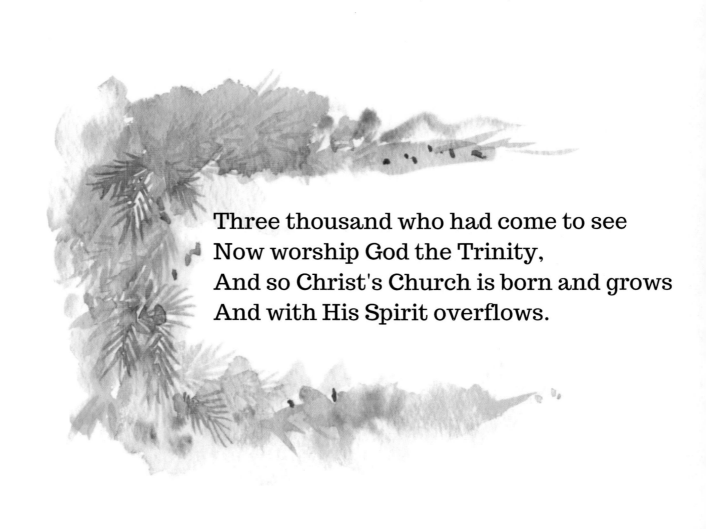

Three thousand who had come to see
Now worship God the Trinity,
And so Christ's Church is born and grows
And with His Spirit overflows.

Yes, this is He who spoke of old
Through holy prophets, who foretold

His coming—Heaven's Mighty King,
The Spirit, who renews all things.

Be glad, then! For the Spirit heals
The wounds of sin, and He reveals,
The Trinity to mortal men
And brings us back to Life again.

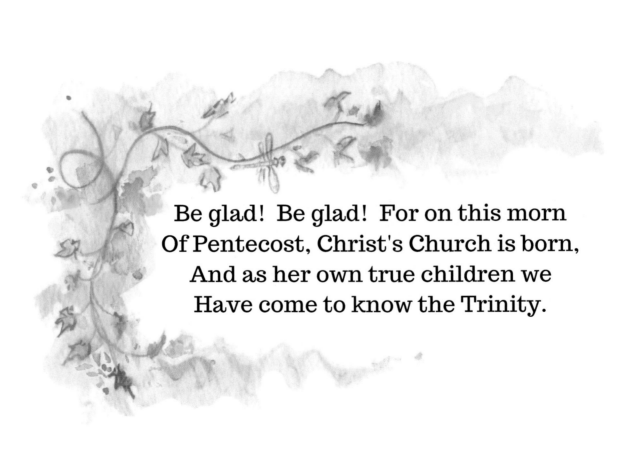

Be glad! Be glad! For on this morn
Of Pentecost, Christ's Church is born,
And as her own true children we
Have come to know the Trinity.

Would you please leave a review at
bit.ly/Review-Pentecost?

I'm always looking for feedback from my
readers and ways to improve!

Thanks so much, and God bless you!

Check out more of Mother Melania's books at
amazon.com/author/mothermelania

Mimi the Mynah
from

The Fearless &
Friends series

*Moses and
the Burning Bush*
from

Old Testament Stories
for Children

*Scooter Gets
the Point*
from

The Adventures of
Kenny & Scooter

ABOUT THE AUTHOR AND ILLUSTRATOR

Mother Melania is the abbess of Holy Assumption Monastery in Calistoga, California. She has enjoyed working with children all of her life. In addition to The Three-Day Pascha series, she has written several other series of children's books, focusing on Scriptural stories and Great Feasts of the Church, and celebrating the virtues.

Bonnie Gillis is an iconographer and illustrator. She lives in Langley, British Columbia, Canada, where her husband, Father Michael, is pastor of Holy Nativity Orthodox Church.

Be glad! Be glad!
   For on this day
God's Spirit comes
   to light our way,
To guide us in through
   Christ the Door,
To dwell in us
   forevermore.

HOLY ASSUMPTION MONASTERY
holyassumptionmonastery.com

Made in the USA
Coppell, TX
03 June 2023

17616208R10019